Registration

Please comple[te] [...] your
Baby Book a[nd] [...].

Baby's name:

Sex:

Address:

CHI number:

Health visitor code:

Your c[ontact de]tails may be used for [...] of
play@ [...] [if you] do not want to p[...]
evalu[...] [che]ck the box. ☐

Registra[tion] [up]date

Please comp[lete the]se details if you change address and give
this form to y[our h]ealth visitor.

Baby's name:

Sex:

Previous [address:]

New addre[ss:]

CHI [num]ber:

New health visitor
code (if changed):

Bookbug

Bookbug encourages parents, carers and children to read together from birth. We gift books to every baby, toddler, 3- and 5-year-old in Scotland in four age-appropriate Bookbug Bags:

- Bookbug Baby Bag (gifted by your health visitor in your baby's first year)
- Bookbug Toddler Bag (gifted by your health visitor when your toddler is aged 1–2 years)
- Bookbug Explorer Bag (gifted at nursery when your child is aged 3 years)
- Bookbug Primary 1 Family Bag (gifted at school when your child is in P1)

If you haven't received your free Bookbug Baby Bag, please ask your health visitor for more details. We also can provide touchy-feely books for children and families with additional support needs.

Bookbug Sessions take place at your local library or community group. These are free, fun-filled sessions for 0–4 year olds. Find details of your local Bookbug Session at **www.scottishbooktrust.com/localbookbugsessions**

Bookbug is run by Scottish Book Trust and funded by the Scottish Government and Creative Scotland. Local Bookbug activity is coordinated by the library service or education department in conjunction with the NHS.

For more information go to
www.scottishbooktrust.com/bookbug

Contents

Benefits of the baby exercise programme

The first seven years of a child's life are the most influential for her* overall development. This programme shows that all movement in babies can be exercise and health related.

Following the programme:

- Starts your baby on a life of healthy exercise.

- Starts daily health related routines.

- Develops good patterns of movement.

- Develops body awareness.

- Encourages your baby's enjoyment of physical activity.

- Encourages talking with your baby.

- Promotes the value of playmates for your baby.

- Encourages loving touch in your family.

- Promotes the value of mums and dads doing daily exercise as role models for your baby.

- Strengthens the relationship between you, the parents, and your baby.

* A note on **his** and **her**:
For ease of reading and not to show any preference, we use both his and her throughout the programme.

How to use your baby programme

- Read 'Facts about your baby' and the 0–3 months section first. You will find this most useful in the first few weeks after your baby's birth.

- Move on to the next section when you think your baby is ready.

- It is important to remember that all newborns are different and like different ways of being handled, for example, not all babies like baby massage. They may prefer other activities like looking, listening and bathing.

- As your baby progresses, move on to the 4–6 months section, then the 7–9 months section, and finally the 10–12 months section. Some babies will enjoy activities beyond the stated age group, others will not be ready to do some things at the stated time.

- This programme gives you a selection of ideas, so you can choose what your baby likes and what suits your family situation.

- Do not feel guilty if you do not follow the suggestions in this programme exactly. You may not have the time or energy to do all that you would like to do. Your parenting ideas may be best for your baby.

- Do not be tempted to rush ahead. Your baby will benefit from repeating favourite activities at any age.

- If you do not understand any of the instructions, ask your health visitor.

Facts about your baby

Baby behaviour

It is important that you learn to observe the sort of mood your baby is in and how to respond.

Your baby's mood	Suitable action
Waking/active **Quiet alert**	Your baby is ready to learn, try games, activities and communication
Looking away or switching off	Stop or change activity because your baby is bored or too tired to continue
Crying*/drowsy	Your baby may need soothing, calming activities like rocking, hugging, stroking or carrying to enable him to sleep or enjoy another activity

Some newborn babies sleep a lot during their first few weeks. Others spend long periods awake. Both types are quite normal.

* If your baby is crying he may first need feeding or changing.

Bone formation

- Remember the bones of babies are more easily injured than those of older children and adults. Babies do not have the strength and reflexes to protect themselves from external forces. Be especially careful when playing energetic games.

- **Baby walkers are not recommended.**

Rates of development

- A baby may lag behind or be ahead in a particular area of development – some babies walk alone at 9 months, some not until 18 months.

- Babies also vary enormously in their individual development patterns, for example, the sitter, the roller, the bottom shuffler. Their muscle strength/tone varies. If your baby 'wobbles' or 'flops' a lot during an activity either he needs extra support or he is not yet ready for that activity.

- If you have been told by health professionals that your baby has special needs, he will benefit very much from this programme but you will need extra help from special health and educational services.

- If you feel that your baby is not progressing as he should and you think there may be something wrong, take your baby to see your doctor or health visitor.

Your baby's movement and learning

- Inactivity slows the ability to learn.

- A baby can only begin to learn through the experience of movement.

- With each newly learned movement, your baby has developed a way to discover the world around her.

- Early movements, which encourage balance and coordination, help her gain new skills and abilities.

- These new skills and abilities will be of use to her both physically and mentally throughout her life.

- It may become apparent in the first year that your baby is left or right handed. Do not attempt to change your baby's naturally dominant hand.

section 1

0–3 months

Bookbug says:
Books, songs and rhymes can easily become part of your day. Why not share a rhyme with your baby during changing or feeding times?

Rocking

Instructions

- Rock your baby to a slow rhythm, such as a rocking chair rhythm.
- If your baby does not like this, try a faster tempo. Many babies prefer this to slow rocking.
- Try dancing around the room with your baby while you hum a simple tune.
- Walks in the pram or rocking the pram may be helpful.

Precautions

- Make sure your baby's head and body are well supported.
- Do not be too energetic, especially after a feed.

benefits

- Soothes your baby who will feel secure in your arms.
- Introduces your baby to a sense of rhythm.
- Your baby is comforted by the sound of your voice.

Skin contact

Instructions

- Give your baby time each day with skin to skin contact, especially if she is bottle fed.

- Gently stroke parts of your baby that are easy to get at, such as the top of head, back of neck, hands and feet.

- Talk to your baby about what you are doing.

Precautions

- Observe your baby carefully to make sure she is enjoying it.

- Stop if she is behaving as if she has had enough handling for the time being.

- If she is partially undressed make sure she is warm enough. Newborn babies become cold very quickly, which can be dangerous.

 # benefits

- Skin to skin contact helps your baby's growth.
- The gentle talking and stroking soothes your baby.
- Introduces your baby to loving touch and baby massage.

Deep bathing

Instructions

- Prepare your baby bath with deep water (approx 30 cm/ 12 inches) which is warm to the inside of your wrist.

- Have a bath towel spread out ready for your baby. Use a baby bath mix or have your baby soap handy. Hair washing may be better done before bathing. Have baby massage oil handy (see page 23).

- Undress your baby and place her slowly and gently in the water. If she is upset, turn her onto her tummy, carefully supporting her body while her face is turned to the side, clear of the water. Wash her when she is relaxed.

- She can stay in the bath as long as she is enjoying it and she is not cold.

- When she has had enough, lift her out and lie her on her tummy. Dry her and massage her gently down her back (see page 33).

Precautions

- Ensure the room is warm.
- Keep your baby's neck as straight as possible and protect her windpipe.
- Ensure that your baby's face is well clear of the water.
- Never leave your baby alone in the bath.

- Be careful of your own back while bathing your baby and carrying water. Make sure your back is as straight as possible.

- You may be more comfortable if you put the bath higher, but make sure you put it on a stable surface.

benefits

- The best way to develop your baby's confidence in water is in the bath.

- The warmth of the water relaxes your baby.

- The depth of water supports your baby's limbs so that she can move them easily.

- Lying on her tummy helps with your baby's startle reflex, stopping her from crying in the bath. Turning to the tummy may not be necessary for all babies.

- Prepares her for baby massage.

Carrying

Instructions

- Take your baby outside daily, if possible, for a pleasant walk either in a baby sling or a pram.
- Choose a baby sling that carries your baby centrally on your chest and has adjustable straps.
- When indoors, vary the way you carry your baby.
- Choose a pram or buggy that has handles high enough to push without stooping forward.

Precautions

- Be careful of injuring your back while carrying your baby. Experiment with the sling until you find a comfortable position for you and your baby.
- If you have an existing back problem seek advice from your doctor before using the sling.
- Make sure her head is well supported and she can breathe easily.
- Do not carry her for long periods in a baby sling as this is not good for her spine or yours.
- As she gets bigger you will have to stop carrying her in a sling or get a stronger type of carrying pack.

 **benefits**

- In a baby sling your baby gets close physical contact, and the warmth, rhythm and noise of your body will make her more contented.

- Fresh air stimulates the body systems of you and your baby so that you both experience a surge of energy.

- Carrying your baby in a variety of positions provides her with movement experience.

Communication

Instructions

- Your baby communicates her needs to you with body movements, facial expressions, crying and vocal noises. Help your baby by putting it into words for her.

- Your voice is very important to your baby. Talk to her a lot about different things, not just baby talk. Try to vary the tone of your voice to keep her attention.

- Sing soothing lullabies to your baby to help settle her. Combine with rocking.

- She is soothed by rhythmic sounds such as a ticking clock or washing machine.

- As she gets older, talk to your baby when she is not looking at you and see if she will turn her head towards the sound.

- Your baby may start to babble at about 6 weeks (along with smiling). Mirror her sounds back to her to have a conversation.

Precaution

- Your baby has a very short attention span and tolerance at this stage. Look for signs that she has had enough.

- Keep your baby at a safe distance from electrical goods.

 # benefits

- Your baby will show a preference at first for her mother's voice because this was a 'womb sound' to her. She will soon get to know the voices of other carers.

- Your baby will begin to recognise different tones of your voice.

- By introducing your baby to different sounds and rhythms you will find out what she likes.

- You are establishing the habit of talking to her.

- She is hearing her language spoken so now she can start to learn it.

- You are giving her positive attention by interpreting her needs.

Looking and seeing

Instructions

- Use your face and simple brightly coloured objects to encourage your baby to focus, follow with her eyes and turn her head.

- A newborn baby can see things clearly 20cm/8 inches away. This range of focus increases to that of an adult by the time she is a year old.

- Your face is the most attractive stimulus for your baby to follow with her eyes.

- Use a variety of colours and shiny objects. Black and white, red and other simple colours are best.

- Patterns on toys should be simple, not too fussy.

- Simple drawings of faces are stimulating.

Variations

Try this activity in different positions:

- When your baby is being nursed.

- When she is on her back.

- When she is on her tummy, once her head is stronger.

 # benefits

- Helps your baby to master movements of the eyes and head.
- Helps to develop your baby's ability to focus on specific objects.
- Increases your baby's awareness of the world around her.

Lying on tummy

Instructions

- Lie your baby on her tummy every day. Place your baby's hands beside her head and gently turn her head to one side. Start with a few minutes and gradually increase the time.

- If your baby does not like lying on her tummy, try lying her across your lap first. Angle her with her head higher than her bottom. Gradually increase the time.

- If your baby is having trouble lifting her head, gently stroke down her back.

- An interesting toy or rattle placed in front of your baby can encourage her to make a bigger effort to lift her head.

- As she gets stronger encourage her to lift her head by placing the palm of your hand under her chest.

Variations

Try this activity in different positions:

- Lie your baby across your lap.

- Lie your baby on your chest, which encourages good eye contact.

Precautions

- Do not overtire your baby with too much time on her tummy to start with.
- Stop as soon as her neck gets tired.
- Do not lie your baby on her tummy to sleep.

benefits

- Strengthens your baby's neck and back.
- Prepares her for learning to crawl.

Baby massage
introduction

Instructions

When

- Six weeks old is a good age to start full baby massage.
- Fit massage into your daily routine, such as bathtime, evening.
- Make sure you choose a time when you are able to relax and take your time.
- Choose a time when your baby is awake, quiet, not particularly hungry and not just after a feed.

Where

- A warm, peaceful room, with perhaps some favourite soothing music.
- Choose a comfortable position to do baby massage, trying to keep as much physical contact with your baby as possible. Make sure you are not bending or twisting your back.
- Lie your baby on a soft towel or sheepskin or cuddly blanket. Have a nappy ready to catch any unexpected presents!

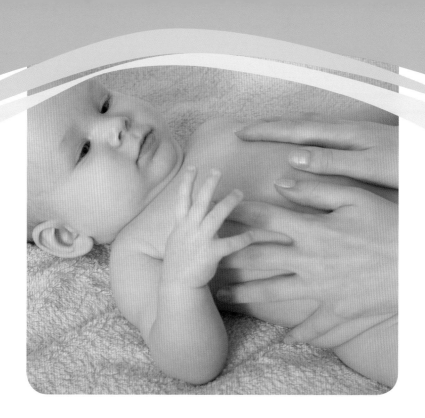

How

- Take off rings and watches.

- Hands must glide on the skin – use natural oils (like grape seed oil), because what is put on the baby's skin may be absorbed into the body. Warm the oil slightly by pouring it onto your hands first.

- Maintain eye contact with your baby as much as possible. Talk to him during the massage.

- Touch should be firm but gentle.

- You may want to practise on an older child or adult to gain confidence.

Precautions

- Do not start baby massage until your baby's cord has healed and he has had a full medical assessment.

- Don't massage your baby if he is unwell.

- Do not start baby massage if your baby has had a vaccination less than a week ago.

- If your baby is premature or has special needs, speak to your health visitor before starting massage.

- If your baby cries and does not seem to like it, leave it and try again the next day. If after three more days of trying he still does not like it, either change your preparation and technique or leave it for another two weeks and try again. Your baby's nervous system may not be ready to handle baby massage yet.

- Do not massage if your baby has broken skin or a skin infection.

- Always be gentle rather than vigorous (see introductory notes on bone formation).

- Note that the face is a very sensitive area and treat with caution (see the following technique pages).

- The palms of the hands and the soles of the feet are also sensitive areas.

- If your baby does not like a particular stroke, leave it out completely. Do more of the strokes that he seems to like.

benefits

- Loving touch and skin contact help your baby to thrive.
- Helps new parents to gain confidence in handling their baby.
- Promotes relaxation of both parents and baby.
- Your baby is learning to enjoy the sensation of being handled and stroked. Touch is important for your baby's physical and emotional wellbeing.
- Develops body awareness.
- Helps babies with colic by breaking the anxiety-pain cycle and improving digestion.
- Improves sleep patterns and settling problems.
- Especially helps the growth and development of premature or low birthweight babies.
- Baby massage is suitable for all growing children, for example, circular stroking of the temples for soothing older children.

Baby massage
techniques

Instructions

- Read the 'Baby massage introduction' section first.

- Make sure your shoulders and hands are relaxed. Your movements should be slow and rhythmical. Keep skin contact as far as possible.

There are two main techniques used:

- Stroking – gliding gently along the surface of the skin.

- Massaging or kneading – gently moving the muscles underneath the skin.

- Repeat each technique 2–3 times, except for face strokes which are one stroke each, because the face is a sensitive area.

- Be flexible – do more of the strokes that your baby obviously enjoys.

- Try to get an even coverage of the whole body. Do each side equally or your baby may feel 'lopsided'.

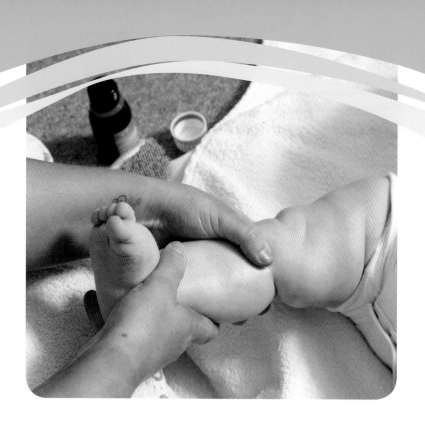

Front of the body

The legs

- Stroke from top of thighs to tips of toes.

- Squeeze muscles gently using your fingers and thumbs from top of thigh to ankle.

- Stroke the ankle area with your palms or fingers.

- Using your thumbs massage the soles of the feet from heel to toe.

- Stroke each toe individually.

The stomach

- Using fingertips or palms, stroke in a clockwise motion around the belly button. The cord should be healed and off. This stroke follows the natural direction of the large bowel.

Note
This stroke and the chest stroke for the diaphragm can be particularly useful for windy, colicky or constipated babies.

The chest

- Starting at the centre front of the chest and using both hands gently stroke in a down and out direction following the spaces between the ribs. This strokes the small muscles running between the ribs, used for breathing.

- Start at the centre front of the chest where the ribs meet at the lower end of the breastbone. Using both thumbs, stroke down and out following the line of the bottom rib. This follows the line of the big breathing muscle or diaphragm.

The arms

- Stroke from shoulder to fingertips.

- Squeeze muscles gently using your fingers and thumbs from top of arm to wrist.

- Massage wrist using thumb and forefinger.

- Stroke the back of the hand using fingers.

- Stroke the palm of the hand using your thumbs. If the hand is clenched do not force it open, leave it closed.

- Stroke each finger using your fingertips and thumbs.

Note
While working on baby's hands encourage him to look at them. Talk to him about what you are doing.

The head (do not use oil)

- Stroke around the top of the head using palms or fingers.
- Stroke down the sides of the face using fingertips.

The face (do not use oil)

Using the fingertips:

- Stroke from the centre of the forehead to the temples **once only**.
- Stroke in circles on the temples.
- Stroke eyebrows from nose to temple **once only**.
- Stroke from nose over cheeks to ears **once only**.
- Stroke from inner corners of eyes down sides of nose to corners of mouth **once only**.

- Stroke from centre of chin out to the ears **once only**.
- Stroke behind the ears from top to bottom.
- Stroke the ears back and front, following their shape.

The neck

Stroke downwards from:

- Ears to shoulders.
- Chin to upper chest.

The whole front

- Using both hands, one for each half of the body, stroke from neck to toes, including arms.

Back of the body

If your baby still does not like lying on his tummy, do these strokes with him across your lap or over your shoulder (see lying on tummy exercise, page 20).

The head

- Using fingers and palms stroke from top of head to base of skull.

The neck and shoulders

Using fingertips very gently massage muscles in a circular motion:

- From top to base of neck on either side of the spine.
- From neck out to shoulders.

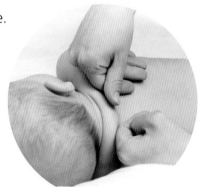

The back

From neck to buttocks:

- Using whole palm of hand stroke downwards.

- Using the fingertips of both hands gently massage muscles in circles moving downwards on either side of the spine.

The legs

- Stroke legs from tops of thighs to toes.

The whole back

From top of head to tips of toes:

- Give several long, light, loving strokes.

To finish

- Wrap your baby and cuddle him for a few minutes before getting him dressed.

Lying on back

Instructions

Place your baby flat on his back, or with his head and shoulders slightly raised on a folded towel.

- Hang a mobile or string a row of pram/cot toys where he can watch them (see 'Suitable toys' section, page 44, for ideas). Give him room to wave his arms about.

- Buy/make sturdy 'touchable' mobiles and place them about 10–15 cm (4–6 inches) above his chest. Eventually he will hit them with his hands, probably by accident (see 'Hand activities' section, page 42).

- Progress to hanging single toys directly in front of him and encourage him to bring his hands to the front and reach out.

- Give him time with his nappy off for leg kicking. If he needs encouragement, press gently on the soles of his feet or put soft foam toys or screwed up newspapers at the foot of the pram/cot so he can feel or hear some 'results' from his kicking efforts.

Precautions

- Many babies love this position. Make sure your baby does not miss out on tummy lying as well.

- Your baby will start to roll to each side and wriggle up and down very quickly while playing this game. Make sure he is safely in his cot, pram or on the floor.

- Do not leave your baby alone if he is lying on a pillow or a folded towel, as there is a risk of suffocation.

benefits

- Interest in the mobile encourages your baby to learn to hold his head in the middle rather than letting it roll to the side.

- This is a good position for leg kicking.

- Touching the mobile helps with hand-eye coordination.

Peek-a-boo

Instructions

- Move from one side of your baby to the other, to encourage her to turn her head.

- Hide your eyes and face (but not your whole head) behind something and surprise her when you reveal your face. She will gradually learn the game.

Variation

- A variation of this can be used during other activities like saying 'Peek-a-boo' when you make eye contact with your baby (as in 'Baby raises' overleaf).

Precautions

- Your baby will take time to learn each game and will enjoy the same game repeated frequently.

- Experiment using different objects and positions to see what she enjoys.

benefits

- Playful communication. Your baby is benefitting from this game although she may not appear to respond at first.
- Encourages your baby to turn her head to locate your position.

Baby raises

Instructions

- Start by sitting on the floor with your knees slightly bent.
- Make sure your back is well supported.
- Place your baby on your lap, facing you. Cup your hands around her shoulders.
- Slowly draw your knees up until she is facing you, then gently return to the starting position.
- Do a maximum of five repeats.
- Talk or sing to your baby during this activity, for example, 'Peek-a-boo'.

Variation

- With your knees slightly bent, gently rock your legs from side to side.

Precautions

- Ensure that your back is well supported and your baby is held securely.
- If your baby does not enjoy this activity, stop and try again another day.

 # benefits

- Encourages your baby to hold her head straight.
- Stimulates early balance reactions.
- Encourages eye contact.

Early sit ups

Instructions

- Start by sitting on the floor with your knees slightly bent.
- Make sure your back is well supported.
- Place your baby on your lap, facing you. Cup your hands around her shoulders.
- Slightly raise her shoulders from your lap. Wait for her to bring her head up in line with her body.
- Return to starting position.
- Do a maximum of five repetitions.

Precautions

- If your baby is not yet able to hold her head well, do not do this exercise. Try again in two weeks.
- Your baby may only be able to cope with one or two movements at first.

 **benefit**

- Strengthens the front of your baby's neck and body getting her ready for sitting up at a later stage.

Hand activities

Instructions

- Encourage your baby to look at his hands and allow him to put them into his mouth.
- Your baby's hands have a grasp reflex for about the first 6 weeks which can be used for putting small rattles in his hand.
- If your baby's grasp reflex is not very strong you can get the same effect by tying a ribbon with little bells on it round his wrist.
- Encourage him to swipe at toys by placing or suspending them within reach of his hands and preferably directly in front of him.
- Encourage him to hold toys. Start to teach him to let go by stroking or gently tapping the back of his hand.

Precautions

- If tying ribbon around your baby's wrist, be careful that it is not tied too tightly. Make sure that any bells are securely sewn on.

- Newborns have strong reflexes for the first 1–3 months which cause them to hold their arms very stiffly in certain positions. Never force your baby's arms to move when he is holding them stiffly. Wait until they loosen up when your baby is in another position. Baby massage is a good way of helping his arms to relax.

42

- A baby puts every toy into his mouth to explore, so toys must be safe (see 'Suitable toys' section overleaf).

benefits

- Increases your baby's awareness of his hands.
- Encourages your baby's eye-hand-mouth activity.
- Swiping at toys is the beginning of your baby's eye-hand object coordination.
- Encourages him to hold his head steady in the middle when attractive toys are placed within his reach, directly in front of him.

Suitable toys

Instructions

- Use natural toys made from wool, cotton and wood as well as plastic.

- Small soft toys, such as teddies, balls.

- Small rattles and teethers in plastic or wood.

- Cotton reels threaded together with wool, laces or ribbons.

- Children's musical boxes.

- Mobiles – bought or home made.

- Baby gyms and play mats.

- Look for toys that move, make a sound and have simple bright colours and patterns.

Precautions

- Look for well known brand names. Look for the CE mark.

- Check the 'suitable for certain ages' label.

- Fillings used in soft toys should be soft, non-toxic, non-flammable and clean. Avoid small pea-like fillings. Check all seams.

- Wooden toys should be made with untreated wood and sanded to avoid splinters.

- Fluids in any toys should be non-toxic in case of accidental breakage.

- Make sure rattles and teethers are smooth and that all parts are secure. All toys or parts of a toy should be large enough to prevent them being swallowed or put in ears or nose.

- Surrounding your baby with too many toys at once will confuse him. Put out one or two things and change the toys when you think he is bored with them.

benefits

- Babies are fascinated by movement and contrasting colours.
- Providing your baby with a variety of interesting toys will stimulate him to want to move and touch.

Role models

Instructions

- Do your postnatal exercise programme with your baby sitting somewhere safe where she can watch you. You should do these exercises daily until your postnatal check-up at six weeks.

- After this, gradually start doing the type of exercise you enjoy. This can be as simple as following a television exercise programme. Clear a space in the lounge and place your baby in a comfortable position.

- If you belong to a gym, sports club or compete in team sports, take your baby along to watch you.

Precautions

Limited by:

- Practical safety considerations at sporting venues.

- The weather.

- Your baby's tolerance. She will get tired after a very short time.

- Your level of fitness. Discuss this with your doctor if you have any concerns.

benefits

- Daily exercise is one of the most enjoyable and beneficial activities that you and your baby can do together.
- By watching you, your baby will learn good movement and coordination skills.
- Your body will become more flexible and you will have more energy.
- Babies will enjoy watching their siblings and the whole family taking part in physical activity, such as games, gardening.

Finding playmates

Instructions

- It is never too soon to introduce your newborn to playmates of her own age.

- Friends made at antenatal classes, the maternity ward, postnatal groups and mother and toddler groups can all be sources of playmates for your baby.

- Place your baby where she can see her playmate, for example, both sitting on parents' knees, or lying beside each other.

- Encourage older siblings to interact with your baby from the earliest days, in the form of 'doing things for' and 'playing with' the baby.

Precautions

- You will want to protect your baby from colds, flu and other illnesses.

- She will get tired very quickly.

- Take care that babies do not hurt each other in their excitement, for example, poking eyes and pulling hair.

 # benefits

- Your baby learns from her playmates.
- Babies may be wary of unfamiliar adults but are quite happy with other babies.
- Babies will look at each other, and may vocalise and reach out.
- If you give them a toy to share they may interact.

section 2

4–6 months

Bookbug says:
Cuddle up and read with your baby. Babies will enjoy being read stories long before they can understand them. It will help your baby feel relaxed, safe and secure.

Baby massage

Instructions

- If you have not already started a daily baby massage programme look at 'Baby massage' in the 0–3 months section (pages 22–33).

- Combine baby massage with body parts games (page 54).

- Try other games of touch using your lips and voice, such as blowing raspberries on your baby's tummy and back, kissing his feet.

- As your baby grows older, massage sessions can take place at any peaceful time.

Precautions

Your baby may be moving around. You might find it easier to massage him:

- Across your lap or over your shoulder when stroking his back.

- In your lap when stroking his front.

 # benefits

- Touch is a very important and enjoyable form of communication for your baby.
- Try using massage to relax or 'loosen up' your baby before trying some of the other exercises.

Body parts game

Instructions

Play games that match touching body parts with action rhymes and songs.

Take your time, your baby will benefit more if you take it slowly.

Kittlin' game

There wis a wee moose
(Hold baby's hand)

Wha wis lookin fur a hoose
(Use index finger to go round the palm)

An' he went creepy, creepy
(Start to walk fingers up baby's arm)

Kittle, kittle, kittle
(Reach the armpit, tickle)

This Is the way...

(to the tune of 'Here we go round the mulberry bush')

This is the way we wash our face,

Wash our face, wash our face,

This is the way we wash our face,

On a cold and frosty morning.

This is the way we wash our hands, etc.

This is the way we wash our feet, etc.

Variations

You will find that the more often you repeat these rhymes, the more your baby will like them.

Other examples:

- This little piggy went to market
- Round and round the garden
- Knock at the door
- Hob shoe hob

(See page 124–133 for the words to these rhymes).

benefits

- **Promotes awareness of body parts.**
- **This is a good communication and enjoyment activity.**

Lying on tummy

Instructions

- Place your baby on his tummy daily.
- When your baby is able to lift his head, tuck his bent arms under his chest and encourage him to push up.
- Place a variety of toys, something different each day, ahead of your baby to encourage him to make his way along the floor.
- Encourage your baby to reach out for the toys.

Variations

If your baby has difficulty pushing his head and shoulders up:

- Try placing a small, rolled up towel under his chest.
- Try placing him across your lap.

Precaution

- If your baby dislikes lying on his tummy, go back to the 'Lying on the tummy' exercises in the 0–3 months section.

 # benefits

- Lets your baby practise pre-crawling movements.
- Strengthens your baby's neck and back against gravity.
- Encourages the development of your baby's arms.
- It is the natural pattern of development for a baby to spend time lying on his tummy on the floor. He learns to move himself, rather than relying on equipment like baby walkers and bouncers.

Rolling over

Instructions

- With your baby lying on his back, encourage him to turn his head to one side.

- Bend his legs up and use his legs to roll him over in the same direction.

- Help him to untangle his underneath arm.

- This is a good exercise to do after each nappy change, doing a different side at each change.

Precautions

- Don't pull on your baby's arms.

- Use his legs to roll him and if he needs extra help give it at the hips.

 **benefits**

- Helps your baby to learn to roll by himself from lying on his back to lying on his front.

- It is good to help your baby in this movement as it can be a hard one to learn by himself. Rolling from his tummy to his back tends to be learned easily and earlier.

Sit ups

Instructions

- Start with your baby lying on his back.
- Cup your hands behind his shoulders and bring him up into a sitting position.
- You can play 'Peek-a-boo' during this exercise.
- Repeat the movement up to five times daily.

Precaution

- Do not carry on with this exercise if your baby's head wobbles backwards when lifting him into a sitting position.

benefits

- Strengthens the front of your baby's neck and body, getting him ready for sitting independently.
- Encourages eye contact.

Baby balance

Instructions

Hold your baby under the armpits. Lift her into a straight up and down position with her feet off the ground.

- Lean your baby to the left, then the right.
- Lean her forwards then just a little way backwards.
- Repeat each movement up to five times.
- You can sing a song while you do this such as See saw, Marjory Daw; Row, row, row your boat (see page 126).

Variation

- Your baby may feel more secure if you sit her on one leg to do these movements.

Precautions

- If your baby does not like this exercise, go back to doing the 'Baby raises' in the first section which gives her more support.
- If she 'flops' (legs, arms or head hang down) your baby may not be ready for this exercise. Try it again in two weeks.

 # benefits

- Strengthens all parts of your baby's body and helps to develop balance.

Knee rides

Instructions

- Sit on a firm chair, with your baby on one of your knees, facing you.

- Use a rhythmical nursery rhyme to move your baby up and down on your knee such as Horsey Horsey, Ride a cock horse, Dance to your daddy (see page 127 for words).

- Suit the movements to the rhythm of the words of the song but don't go too fast.

- Do an extra large bounce on important words.

Variation

- Dancing around the room with your baby in your arms to a rhythmical song.

Precautions

- Your baby must be able to hold his head steady to do these activities.

- Do not keep playing a game if he does not like it. Some babies enjoy more energetic games than others.

 # benefits

- Gives your baby a sensation of moving his body through space.
- He learns to locate where his body is in space.
- He loves the playful communication with his parent whom he trusts.

Bathing activities

Instructions

- Continue to use the 'Deep bathing' technique as in the 0–3 months section but you will need to move on to using the method in the big bath or taking your baby into the big bath with you.

- Support your baby's head as in the deep warm bathing technique or however you find comfortable. Move her gently backwards and forwards in the water.

- Encourage arm and leg movements.

- Gently squeeze a trickle of water over the back of her head.

- Use a container to pour water over her head, shoulders and back. Avoid her face.

- Use lots of floating toys to make the bath a fun, interesting place.

Precautions

- Ensure the bath is at a suitable temperature for your baby.

- Be particularly careful to gradually introduce water to your baby's face as this is a very sensitive area.

- If you are keen to take your baby to the swimming pool but lack confidence in water yourself, you should find out about classes for yourself first. If you are nervous about water, this feeling will communicate itself to your baby.

benefit

- Continues to build your baby's confidence in water.

Hand activities

Instructions

- Encourage your baby to reach out and grasp by bringing her arms forward gently from the shoulder.

- Encourage her to learn to let go with her hands. Try different sized toys. Place your palm so her hand and the object rest on it and she will be able to let go of it.

- Use the same words or phrases while you do this, such as 'Ta','Give it to me'.

- Give toys to your baby from directly in front. This will help her learn to use both arms together while looking at the toy.

- Encourage her to pass toys from one hand to another.

- Give her a toy that requires her to hold on with both hands, such as a soft ball.

- Use different shapes and textures.

Precautions

- Your baby may still have some newborn stiffness in her arms. It is best to encourage her to bring her arms forward by moving the arm from the shoulder rather than pulling on her hand. Never force her arms forward. Trying another position for the activity may help.

- She may find it difficult to learn to let go, or she may let toys go by accident.

 # benefits

- Improves hand skills by learning to let go.
- Your baby benefits from hearing repeated words which will help her to learn language.
- Begins to coordinate hands and eyes.
- Different shapes and textures will help your baby's awareness of her hands.

Suitable toys

Instructions

- Toys suitable for mouthing.

- Experiment to find the right sized object that your baby can hold on to.

- Suspend toys within reaching distance across her pram, cot, etc. so that she can reach and hold them.

- Suction toys and weighted toys that stand on the ground and don't fall over.

- Activity centres.

- Home made toys – simple containers with different everyday items sealed in them. Clear plastic is good so that your baby can see the items, for example, lentils or pasta shapes in plastic tubs.

Precautions

- As your baby will now be mouthing everything, avoid toys which are small enough to go right into her mouth. These may choke her.

- Check all objects that might go into your baby's mouth for wear and tear and sharp edges. Also check that any inks, dyes, paints and fillings are non-toxic.

- Do not let her play with cracked or broken plastic cartons, long pieces of string or plastic bags.

- Only let her play with wrapping paper when someone is with her.

- Dolls should have soft bodies with embroidered or painted on faces. Any eyes, noses, hair, buttons and so on should be firmly and safely attached.

- Check the 'suitable for certain ages' label.

- Check the CE mark.

benefits

- **Your baby likes toys that she can put to her mouth to explore.**
- **Your baby likes to feel different textures and shapes.**
- **She likes toys that make a noise and move.**

Communication

Instructions

- Your voice is still the most important sound to your baby. Talk to her about what you are doing.

- Imitate your baby's first babbling sounds. You may hear 'ba', 'ma' and 'da' sounds.

- Read lots of things to her, from baby books to sections of the newspaper.

- Vary your tone of voice to keep her interested.

- Try to spend some time each day face to face with your baby to talk and recite rhymes. Use rhymes frequently.

- Use your lips and voice to blow and make noises on your baby's tummy, neck and back.

Precautions

- Watch for signs that your baby is 'overloaded'.

- Try not to talk too fast and remember pauses are important.

- Have one sound going on at a time so that your baby doesn't become confused, for example, switch off TV when reading to your baby.

 # benefits

- Imitating your baby's sounds teaches taking turns.
- Talking to your baby and reading different things to her is the best way to encourage her speech.

section 3

7–9 months

Bookbug says:
Bring your baby along to fun, free
Bookbug Sessions at your local
library for stories, songs and rhymes!
To find details of your local session
go to **www.scottishbooktrust.
com/babies-early-years/parents/
localbookbugsessions**

Baby massage

Instructions

- It is not too late to start doing baby massage but it is a little more difficult to be confident with a baby on the move.

- A baby on the move needs to be massaged in positions like over your shoulder, across your lap or sitting in your lap.

- You probably won't be able to do a full body massage in one session. It is quite all right to do it in bits and pieces as you are able to catch hold of your baby. He does not need to be fully undressed.

- The strokes you will find most useful are top and back of head, temple circling, neck and back stroking and massaging, long body and leg strokes and foot massage (see pages 26–33 for a description of these techniques).

Precautions

- If your baby is very active, do not keep trying. Leave doing baby massage until he is older and more content to stay in one place for a period of time.

- Using oil may be more of a danger than a help now, making your baby very slippery to handle if active.

 # benefits

- Although your baby is very much on the move by now, time spent relaxing is beneficial for both of you.

- It is good to keep the massage routine going even if it is very varied now.

- It can be helpful for you to be able to soothe and calm your baby using massage.

Sit ups

Instructions

- Start with your baby lying on his back. Hold him by his hands and pull him up into a sitting position.

- Use repeated phrases, such as 'Up you come!', 'Down you go!'

- Repeat up to five times daily.

- If your baby has a strong grip you can progress this exercise by encouraging him to grip your thumbs to pull up to sit.

Precautions

- Your baby must have good head control before you try this exercise.

- If your baby's arms feel floppy, go back to the 'Sit up' exercises in the 4–6 months section (page 60).

 # benefits

- Strengthens the front of your baby's neck, body, shoulders and arms.
- Encourages eye contact and develops anticipation.

Learning to sit

Instructions

- Pull your baby to a sitting position (see 'Sit ups', page 78).
- Place his hands on the floor in front of him for support.
- Help him to keep his balance in this position.
- Once he can prop herself well in this position, encourage him to reach for toys to the front and sides of him.

Precautions

- Your baby must be able to pull to a sitting position before trying this activity.
- Do not try this if his head and arms are still wobbly.
- Your baby will fall while learning this new skill. Be ready to catch him.
- He may only manage short periods of this activity.

 **benefits**

- He is beginning to support himself in sitting.
- He is learning balancing skills.

Pre-crawling

Instructions

- Your baby is ready to try this when he can lie on his tummy and push his head and shoulders up.

- Place toys around him to encourage him to reach out with one hand.

- Place toys further away to encourage him to wriggle on his tummy to reach them.

- When he is pushing up on his hands, gently guide his knees under his body. This will raise his bottom into a crawling position.

- Use your hands to steady him around the hips in the crawling position. Encourage him to reach out for toys with one hand at a time.

Precautions

- Work in a safe area, with no hard edges where he may bump his head.

- You may need to give extra support around his body when he first reaches out with one hand.

 # benefits

- He is beginning to organise his balance and movement, getting ready for crawling.
- He is beginning to move towards objects by himself.

Crawling

Instructions

Practise crawling as much as possible.

Once your baby is crawling on her knees try to get her to crawl:

- over a threshold
- under a chair
- up a step
- over different surfaces, such as carpet, lino, grass.

Precautions

- Check the floor surfaces for sharp objects. Dress your baby in durable trousers.
- Look for unstable furniture in the room.
- Supervise all activities that involve steps.

A note on your baby's development

- A small percentage of babies never actually crawl but think of other ways to get themselves about like rolling, creeping or bottom shuffling. Other babies just sit until they are ready to stand up and walk. These are normal variations of development, however continue to offer the opportunity to crawl.

 # benefits

- Crawling is good practice for your baby to coordinate the movement of her arms and legs.
- Crawling over, under and up things is an extra demand on your baby's coordination.
- Your baby is more aware of her body's size when trying to get under and around objects.
- Research shows that crawling is a very important stage in the development of a baby's brain.

Pull ups

Instructions

- Select a suitable piece of solid low furniture for your baby to practise pulling herself up to stand.
- Put some attractive toys on it to encourage her into trying the movement.
- Help her by guiding her movements with your hands.
- Encourage her to use her upper arms and shoulders to reach out, then use your hands to guide her hips to a standing position.

Precautions

- Have the piece of furniture against a wall or a sofa so that it is very stable.
- Have no sharp edges. Chrome or glass tops are unsuitable for babies.
- The piece of furniture should be at your baby's waist height or lower.

 # benefits

- Teaches your baby an important step – getting off the floor to standing in the correct way.
- Teaches her an exercise which makes her independent, she is not reliant on parent to stand her up each time.

Ankle rides

Instructions

- Sit in a chair. Cross your legs and sit your baby on your lower leg. Hold her upper body. Lift your leg up and down to the rhythm of a bouncing rhyme, such as:

  Humpty Dumpty sat on a wall

  Humpty Dumpty had a great fa-a-a-ll

  All the King's horses and all the King's men

  Couldn't put Humpty together again
  (Lower ankle to floor on 'fall')

Precaution

- Your baby needs good head and body strength to cope with this game.

benefits

- Develops awareness of body movement through space.
- Strengthens body and head as your baby works to keep her head and body straight.
- Develops sense of rhythm and fun.

Big toys

Instructions

- Your baby may like a simple rocking toy to sit in or on, with support.

- He may be ready for a small swing with a well padded and supported seat.

Precautions

- Make sure your baby is ready for this exercise, that his head and body are strong enough.

- Move the swing or rocking horse slowly to start with and if he does not like it, stop.

- Try using rubber stoppers to limit the rocking movement initially.

- Make sure he is well supported in the seat.

- Baby walkers are not recommended.

 **benefits**

- Develops your baby's confidence in heights.
- Develops his enjoyment of rhythm and movement in space.

Hide and seek

Instructions

- Partly hide yourself behind furniture or doors and let your baby come to you. Call him if you need to.

- Use lots of facial expressions and vary your tone of voice.

- Play hiding games with a toy. When you bring the toy out again, act surprised and use the same phrase, such as 'here it is' or 'found it'.

- Try using action rhymes, such as Two little dicky birds, Ten little soldiers, Ten little fingers (see pages 128–129 for words and actions).

Precautions

- Don't completely hide yourself or your baby will get worried.

- Your house and furniture should be well 'baby proofed' by now – double check for any hazards.

 # benefits

- Teaches your baby about the size of your body, toys, furniture and his body.
- Games are a good way to stimulate him to move around.
- Your baby learns anticipation and early language skills.

Water activities

Instructions

- When your baby has good sitting balance, she will want to sit and play with toys in a much shallower bath.

- Concentrate on fun and games at this stage with a variety of toys for pouring, etc.

- If you are keen to take your baby swimming, take her for a visit to the pool first to introduce her to the strange atmosphere and smell.

Precautions

- Your baby's sitting balance might be very good but still never leave her alone in the bath.

- Non-slip rubber mats can be useful at this stage.

Continue introducing your baby to water confidence and play activities until she is around four years old. At that stage she can begin to learn swimming strokes.

Before taking your baby to a swimming pool, check:

- Is your baby ready for a pool – confident in the bath at home?

- Is there a separate parent and baby session?

- Is there a family changing room?

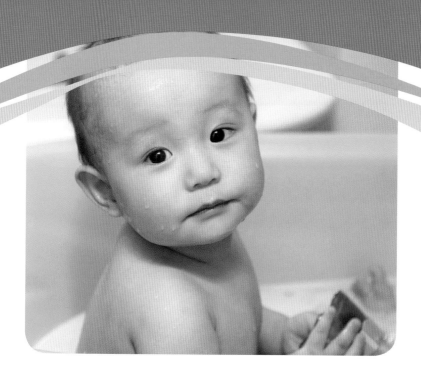

- Is the water warm enough?
- Is the air temperature warm by the pool and in the changing room?
- Is the chlorine level okay for your baby?
- Is your baby free of any type of infection, especially ear, chest or tummy?
- Are you confident in water yourself?

benefits

- Your baby will enjoy lots of water play.
- This will offer her a new range of interesting experiences.

Hand activities

Instructions

- Continue to offer your baby opportunities to grasp a toy with both hands.

- Continue to encourage her to pass a toy from one hand to the other.

- Continue to offer her different shapes and textures.

- She will learn to knock over and pull apart toys. Put them back together for her. She will learn how to do it by watching you.

- Encourage pouring action in water play.

Precautions

- Your baby will still put everything that she picks up into her mouth. She is a lot more mobile now so more precautions are necessary around the home.

 **benefits**

- Your baby's grasp and release will improve with a variety of objects to practise on.
- She starts to use her hands in separate skilled movements, rather than her whole arm in a large movement.

97

Suitable toys

Instructions

- Once your baby can crawl, he enjoys toys that push or roll along, like balls.

- Provide simple, homemade musical instruments, for example, drums made from metal pans, upturned ice cream containers and wooden spoons.

- Toys that pull apart, such as nesting beakers, plastic rings on a column, peg people for lifting out of holes, pull-apart large plastic shapes.

- Small safe objects for practising picking up, such as rice crispies.

Precautions

- Wooden toys are excellent but check that they are made of untreated wood and have smooth edges.

- Check toy boxes regularly and throw out any toy that is broken or dangerous.

- Check the 'suitable for certain ages' label.

- Check for the CE mark.

 # benefits

- Toys that roll along the floor stimulate your baby to move after them.
- He continues to learn musical rhythm.
- He has to learn pulling apart before he can learn putting together.
- He is beginning to learn a skilled pinch grasp.

Communication

Instructions

- Listen to your baby's, cheerful early morning chatter and his amazing range of sounds.

- Lie down face to face with your baby and repeat each sound he makes. Take your time and enjoy your simple conversation together. The sounds you are most likely to hear are: ha, ba, mu, me, ah, da, ma, oh, ga, pa.

- He may now move his whole body and babble in response to music. Encourage this.

A note on your baby's development

- Your baby's understanding is developing quickly. He is now beginning to realise that people, things and events are separate from himself. He now wants the toy back that he has dropped under his cot, he now follows people with his eyes until they are out of sight and waits for them to appear again.

- He can now remember earlier experiences and is beginning to anticipate events.

- He can be very uncooperative if he doesn't want you to take something away or he doesn't feel like being dressed or fed.

 **benefits**

- Your baby loves to communicate and he will really enjoy having you listen to what he says.
- His sense of rhythm is encouraged.

section 4

10–12 months

Bookbug says:
Read a story and sing a lullaby to your baby before bed. It is a great way to end the day on a calm, positive note.

First steps

Instructions

- Give your baby opportunities to stand at a low table or couch and give him interesting toys to play with.

- Encourage him to use one hand to support at first, then encourage him to use both hands to play while leaning against the couch. Eventually he should be able to use both hands while not leaning against the couch at all.

- Encourage him to walk sideways around the couch using his hands for support.

- Encourage a few steps towards you alongside the couch.

- If he falls, give him time to get up by himself.

Precautions

- Check the height of table or couch being used. It needs to be at your baby's waist height or slightly lower. Avoid glass tables or sharp edges.

- Check that the piece of furniture used is stable.

- If your baby is unable to pull himself up to standing, refer back to 'Pull ups' exercise in the 7–9 month section (page 86), and work on that.

- Watch your baby closely to stop falls, bumps and cuts.

benefits

- Helping your baby to develop standing balance and strength while standing at a couch or table will get him ready for walking.

Walking

Instructions

- Practise walking with both hands held forwards at first.
- Practise walking with one hand held, only when your baby's balance has improved.
- Encourage independent walking by taking a few steps between two adults who he trusts.
- Use plenty of encouraging words.

Precautions

- Bring yourself down to your baby's level on your knees to avoid strain on your back.
- Watch him closely at this stage – a fall could lead to a loss of confidence from which he could take 1–2 months to recover.
- Do not worry if he is slow to walk independently. As long as he is moving around (crawling) he is still able to explore his environment.
- Walk slowly with your baby when walking with him. Remember he has to take three steps to every one of yours.

 **benefit**

- Practising with plenty of support and help will boost your baby's confidence.

Stair climbing

Instructions

- Encourage your baby to climb onto the couch and teach her how to get down backwards.

- Teach her how to climb stairs and how to get down backwards, feet first.

Precautions

- All stairways should be gated at the top and the bottom.

- All climbing activities should be supervised until at least two years of age.

- Your baby is probably in overdrive by now – crawling, climbing and possibly walking.

- She wants to climb everything. She can figure out how to shift furniture to climb even higher. She gets stuck easily, has a short attention span and no sense of danger, so she needs a lot of supervision and protection from injury at this stage.

benefit

- Climbing is a further demand on your baby's crawling coordination skills.

Action songs

Instructions

- Do lots of baby's favourite action games, such as ankle rides, bouncing games.
- Continue to play hide and seek.
- Use songs and action rhymes to encourage copying, such as Clap clap hands and The doughnut song (see page 123). He will copy better if you go slowly.

Father and mother and Uncle John

Father and mother and
Uncle John
Went to market one by one
(Jog your baby gently on
your knee)
Father fell off
(Dip him to one side)
Mother fell off
(Dip him to the other side)
But Uncle John went on,
and on
And on, and on, and on.
(Jog your baby faster
on your knee)

Peter Rabbit

(Sing to the tune of 'John Brown's Body')

Little Peter Rabbit's got a fly upon his nose x 3
(Touch baby's nose on the word 'nose')
He swished it
(swipe with right hand in front of your face)
And he swashed it
(swipe with left hand in front of your face)

And the fly flew away
(flap your hands)
Floppy ears and curly whiskers x 3
(Hands sticking up from your head like rabbit's ears, then stroke imaginary whiskers in circular motion)
And he swished it and he swashed it
And the fly flew away.
(Actions as above)

 **benefits**

- Encourages the natural tendency of children of this age to move while encouraging body awareness and rhythm.

Ball skills

Instructions

- Sit on the floor opposite your baby with your legs apart, almost touching her feet with your feet. Roll a soft light ball along the floor. Encourage her to roll it back to you.

- Kneel or sit facing your baby. Give her a small light ball the right size for her hand. A screwed up piece of paper may be best. Encourage her to throw it, then roll it back to her.

- If your baby does not play at first, show her what to do with another person.

- Your baby may keep the ball and not roll it back as this is a possessive stage. It will pass. Try again in a few weeks.

Precautions

- Always roll the ball back to your baby. Throwing a ball at a baby can be very frightening for her. It may put her off balance and cause her to fall. She will not be coordinated enough to catch the ball to stop it hitting her body.

 **benefits**

- This encourages early development of ball skills.
- The use of light, correctly sized balls makes development of catching and throwing easier.

Outdoors

Instructions

- Introduce your baby to sandpit games. Try various containers for pouring sand or building sandcastles.

- Play in a paddling pool in summer. Use toys that float and are fun to tip when full of water.

- Your baby will enjoy trips to the park and playground. Help her play on the swings and chute. Talk to her about the grass, trees, flowers and leaves and let her touch them.

Precautions

- Always supervise your baby closely outdoors, especially if playing with water.

- Paddling pools can be topped up with hot water after filling to about 8 inches (20 cms), so that they are comfortably warm.

- Empty paddling pools after each use so they do not become a drowning hazard.

- Sandpits need to be covered to keep animals out. A firm cover can be used as an additional playing surface.

benefits

- This will provide new sensory experiences with sand, water, movement and nature.
- She is beginning to learn more about the world around her.

Hand activities

Instructions

- Encourage your baby to pick up rice crispies or crumbs of bread in a pinch grip between thumb and fingers.

- Encourage her to poke her forefinger into holes and other objects which are safe.

- Encourage her to use two toys together, such as a pot and spoon, interesting cups.

- Once your baby can release her grip, play games of give and take.

- Give her lots of opportunities to watch adults using their hands.

- Play singing games and use action rhymes such as Incy wincy spider (see page 131).

- Encourage first attempts with crayon and paper. You will need to hold the paper for her.

- Encourage pouring sand in the sandpit and water play.

- Let her try to feed herself, using her fingers. Vary the textures of food such as cheese, toast, jelly, yoghurt.

Precautions

- See 'Suitable toys' section for a choice of toys to give.
- More safety precautions will be needed as your baby's hand skills develop rapidly, for example, socket covers, cupboard locks.
- Supervise feeding closely.
- Supervise crayon attempts closely.

 **benefits**

- Grasping toys in the palm of her hand will progress to a more skilled grip between fingers and thumb.
- She develops the ability to handle more than one object at a time. Your baby begins to learn to feed herself.

Suitable toys

Instructions

- Provide toys that push along. Use something lower, heavier and stable that moves slowly to start with. Use lighter push along toys later.

- Provide simple ride on, push along toys with front wheels that only travel in a straight line.

- A wooden jigsaw puzzle with little pegs make it easy to lift out the pieces.

- Provide simple shape sorters.

- Provide books with thick cardboard pages, or made from cloth or vinyl.

Precautions

- Little pegs on wooden jigsaw puzzle pieces can break off.

- Pull along cords could become wrapped around your baby's neck. Cords should be as short as possible. Check that there is no possibility of slipknots forming. Remove cords from bedtime toys.

- Pull and push toys with rigid handles should have a protective knob securely attached at the end of the handle.

- Make sure your baby is ready to use a toy or it will only frustrate him. Put it away for a bit longer if it does.
- Check the 'suitable for certain ages' label.
- Check the CE mark.

benefits

- Encourages enjoyment of movement.
- Encourages development of fine hand skills.
- Introduces your baby to books.

Communication

Instructions

- Talk to your baby about things in his world and give them names.

- He will start to respond to his own name about this time.

- He may have some understanding of the word 'no' although he may not respond by stopping what he is doing.

- If you use short sentences and emphasise and repeat key words, he may begin to try to say them, 'Mmm biscuit. Do you want a biscuit?' He may say 'bikkit'.

- Use a range of words, not just names of things. Use action words such as 'walk' and describing words such as 'hot'.

- Try to structure his musical activities by sitting down, playing instruments with him and clapping, singing and marching to the beat.

A note on your baby's development

- Your baby now starts to show wariness and caution when meeting adults he doesn't know well. This is a normal stage and probably because he is still developing the ability to remember familiar people.

- As your baby continues to develop he increases his understanding and his memory. This improves his ability to communicate with you. He appreciates the games and routines that you have built up together and they give him a sense that life is orderly and secure.

 # benefits

- Your baby is imitating your language. He is starting to recognise and use your rhythms, accents and facial expressions. He will say his first word at any time now.

- Repeating key words strengthens your baby's vocabulary.

- Your baby learns he can please you by doing some things and that there are some things that don't please you.

- Musical rhythm is encouraged more.

Songs and rhymes

Body parts game – from page 54

This little piggy

This little piggy went to market
(wiggle baby's big toe)

This little piggy stayed at home
(wiggle second toe)

This little piggy had roast beef
(wiggle third toe)

This little piggy had none
(wiggle fourth toe)

This little piggy cried
"wee-wee-wee"
(wiggle little toe)

All the way home
(run your fingers up to
baby's tummy and tickle it)

Hob, shoe, hob

Hob, shoe, hob

Hob, shoe, hob

Here a nail

There a nail

And that's well shod
(A foot patting rhyme – Pat the
sole of each foot in turn)

Round and round the garden

Round and round the garden

Like a teddy bear
(run your finger around baby's palm)

One step, two step
(walk fingers slowly up baby's arm)

Tickle you under there
(tickle baby under the arm)

Knock at the door

Knock at the door
(gently tap baby's forehead)

Peep in
(point to the eyes)

Lift up the latch
(touch the end of baby's nose)

Walk in
(touch baby's mouth)

Chin chopper, chin chopper
(touch baby's neck under the chin)

Chin, chin chin
(tickle baby there)

Baby balance songs – Page 62

Move baby slowly, in time to the rhythm:

See saw Marjory Daw

See saw, Marjory Daw
Johnny shall have a new master
He shall have but a penny a day
Because he can't work any faster

Row your boat

Row, row, row your boat
Gently down the stream
Merrily, merrily, merrily, merrily
Life is but a dream

Knee ride songs and rhymes – page 64

Move your baby up and down on your knee in time to the rhythm:

Horsey Horsey

Horsey Horsey don't you stop

Just let your feet go clippety clop

The tail goes swish and the wheels go round

Giddy-up we're homeward bound

Ride a cock horse

Ride a cock horse to Banbury Cross

To see a fine lady upon a white horse

Rings on her fingers and bells on her toes

She shall have music wherever she goes

Dance to your daddy

Dance to your daddy

My little babby

Dance to your daddy

My little lamb

You shall have a fishy

On a little dishy

You shall have a fishy

When the boat comes in

Hide and seek action rhymes – page 92

Two little dicky birds

Two little dicky birds sitting on a wall
(hold out fists with index finger raised)

One named Peter, one named Paul
(shake each finger in turn for Peter and Paul)

Fly away Peter
(put one hand behind your back)

Fly away Paul
(put other hand behind your back)

Come back Peter

Come back Paul
(bring hands back one at a time, index fingers raised)

Ten little soldiers

Ten little soldiers standing straight
(hold up both hands)

Ten little soldiers open the gate
(swivel hands to face each other)

Ten little soldiers all in a ring
(put your wrists together and spread fingers as if holding a ball)

Ten little soldiers bow to the king
(bend fingers over)

Ten little soldiers dance all day
(dance hands and fingers)

Ten little soldiers hide away
(hide hands behind back)

Ten little fingers

I have ten little fingers

And they all belong to me
(hold up hands and wiggle
fingers)

I can make them do things

Would you like to see?

I can shut them up tight
(clench fists tightly)

Or open them wide
(open fingers as wide as possible)

Put them all together
(interlink fingers)

Or make them all hide
(put your hands behind
your back)

I can make them jump higher
(raise hands in the air)

I can make them jump low
(bring them down again)

I can fold them quietly

And hold them all just so
(fold hands in your lap)

Action songs and games – page 110

Clap, clap hands

Clap, clap hands, one, two, three
(clap your hands in rhythm)

Place your hands upon your knee
(touch your knee)

Lift them high to touch the sky
(hold both hands in the air)

Clap, clap hands and away
they fly
(shake your hands and wiggle
your fingers)

The doughnut song

I went to the bakers to get
something to eat

I felt so hungry from my head
to my feet
(gently pat head then feet)

So I picked up the doughnut
and wiped off the grease

And handed the lady a
penny piece

Well she looked at the penny

Then she looked at me

She said kind sir you can
plainly see

There's a hole in your penny,
there's a hole right through
(peek through hole made by
your hands)

Says I, there's a hole in your
doughnut too!

Hand activity rhyme – page 116

Incy wincy spider

Incy wincy spider

Climbed up the spout
(walk your fingers up in front
of you)

Down came the rain
(lower you arms, wiggling your
fingers in like rain)

And washed the spider out
(palms down, scissor your arms
in front of you)

Out came the sunshine
(raise your hands)

Dried up all the rain
(bring your arms down and out,
making a circle)

Incy wincy spider

Climbed up the spout again
(walk your fingers up in front of
you again)

Some other action songs and rhymes you may enjoy with your baby

A wee wee man

A wee wee man came over the hill
(place two fingers at the back of baby's head and walk them up and over the top of his head, stopping at the forehead)

He chappit at the door
(tap lightly on his forehead)

He keekit in
(look in his eyes)

He liftit up the latch
(brush the end of his nose with your finger)

And he walkit in
(touch his lips)

Head, shoulders, knees and toes

Head, shoulders, knees and toes, knees and toes

Head, shoulders, knees and toes, knees and toes

And eyes and ears and mouth and nose

Head, shoulders, knees and toes, knees and toes
(touch each part of the body as you sing)

Pat-a-cake

Pat-a-cake, pat-a-cake

Baker's man
(clap baby's hands in time)

Bake me a cake

As fast as you can

Pat it and prick it
(pat palm of baby's hand, and
pretend to prick it)

And mark it with B
(trace a B on it)

And put it in the oven
(mime putting a cake into
an oven)

For baby and me

Jelly on the plate

Jelly on the plate

Jelly on the plate

Wibble, wobble

Wibble, wobble

Jelly on the plate
(wobble baby gently
on your knee)

133

Bibliography

Aukett A. (1981) **Baby Massage** David Bateman Auckland

Berdychova J. (1983) **Parent and Children's Exercise Booklet** Olympia Prague

Dalley M. (1983) **Moving and Growing** Canadian Institute of Child Health Ottawa

Kitzinger S. (1989) **The Crying Baby** Penguin London

Manolson A. (1992) **It Takes Two To Talk** Hanen Centre Toronto

Martin E. (1988) **Baby Games** Running Press Philadelphia

Montagu A. (1971) **Touching – the Human Significance of the Skin** Harper and Row New York

Muthukumaraswamy G. (1990) **Kiwi Baby** Sport Waikato Hamilton

Petrie P. (1987) **Baby Play: activities for discovery and development during the first year of life** Doubleday New York

Whiteford B. and Poldent M. (1987) **Post Natal Exercises – A Six Month Fitness Programme for Mother and Baby** Century Hutchinson London

Picture credits